beetle bailey,
Is That All?

by
MORT WALKER

tempo
books

GROSSET & DUNLAP
A FILMWAYS COMPANY
Publishers • New York

beetle bailey, #14
Is That All?

DO YOU THINK THEY'LL LIKE MY NEW PROPOSAL AT THE STAFF MEETING, SIR?

WHO KNOWS?

7-22

AS THEY SAY ON MADISON AVENUE, "RUN IT UP THE FLAGPOLE AND SEE IF ANYONE SALUTES IT."

JUST A MINUTE, PLEASE

/CLICK

7-8

THE ELECTRONIC AGE HAS SOME SINGULAR SATISFACTIONS

I HAVE LT. FUZZ ON HOLD

MORT WALKER

IT ALWAYS AMAZES ME HOW SARGE CAN DO THAT

DO WHAT?

6-30

HOLD A BAG OF POTATO CHIPS BETWEEN HIS KNEES WHILE WATCHING A DRACULA MOVIE, AND NOT BREAK ONE CHIP

CHIP

MORT WALKER

DARN
THAT
SARGE
!

HOW MANY TIMES HAVE I TOLD
YOU NOT TO THROW OUT YOUR
PANCAKE SYRUP BOTTLES WITH
THE CAP OFF?!

Mort
Walker

AREN'T WE HAVING LUNCH BEFORE WE PLAY?!

NO. THE FIRST TEE IS OPEN, WE CAN TEE RIGHT OFF!

10-3

THE FAIRWAYS LOOK LIKE THEY HAVEN'T BEEN CUT IN A WEEK

HOW'S THE ROUGH, SARGE?

NEEDS A LITTLE SALT!

Mort WALKER

8-29

9-17